Reading
Practice

PaRragon

Bath • New York • Cologne • Melbourne • Delhi
Hong Kong • Shenzhen • Singapore

Helping your child

- Remember that the activities in this book should be enjoyed by your child. Try to find a quiet place to work.

- Your child does not need to complete each page in one go. Always stop before your child grows tired and come back to the same page another time.

- It is important to work through the pages in the right order because the activities get progressively more difficult.

- In this book, we talk about letters as having names and sounds. For capital letters, we use the letter names (the names of the letters when we recite the alphabet): 'ay', 'bee', 'see', 'dee', 'ee', 'eff', 'jee'. For small letters, we use the letter sounds (the sounds of the letters when we read a word): 'aaa', 'b-b-b', 'ck', 'duh', 'eh', 'fff', 'guh'.

- The answers to the activities are on page 32.

- Always give your child lots of encouragement and praise.

- Remember that the gold stars are a reward for effort as well as for achievement.

This edition published by Parragon Books Ltd in 2017

Parragon Books Ltd
Chartist House
15-17 Trim Street
Bath BA1 1HA, UK
www.parragon.com

Copyright © Parragon Books Ltd 2002–2017

Written by Nina Filipek
Illustrated by Simon Abbot and Adam Linley
Educational Consultant: Geraldine Taylor

ISBN: 978-1-4748-7618-6

Printed in China

Contents

Sound play

Read the sentences and make the fun sounds.

Hisssssss like a snake.

Go **wheeeee** down the slide.

Whooooooo like a ghost!

Ch-ch-ch-ch-ch like a steam train.

Buzzzzz like a busy bee.

Tick-tock, tick-tock like a clock.

Note for parent: At the end of each sentence, ask your child: 'What was that sound again?'
Encourage your child to listen for sounds at home too.

Sing a song

Sing the song and make the animal noises.

Old Macdonald had a farm.
E-I-E-I-O!
And on that farm
he had some cows.
E-I-E-I-O!
With a moo-moo here and a moo-moo there.
Here a moo, there a moo, everywhere a moo-moo!
Old Macdonald had a farm.
E-I-E-I-O!

And on that farm
he had some pigs...

Oink, oink!

Neigh, neigh!

And on that farm
he had some horses...

Baa, baa!

And on that farm
he had some sheep...

Note for parent: Ask your child: 'What sound does a pig make?', 'What sound does a horse make?', 'What sound does a sheep make?' and so on.

5

Letter sounds

The letters of the alphabet have different sounds. Trace each small letter with a pencil. Say the sound of the letter at the start of each word.

a a apple

b b bed

c c car

d d dog

e e egg

f f fish

g g gate

h h hat

i i insect

j j jug

k k king

l l ladder

Note for parent: Say the sound of each letter as you would pronounce it in the word.

m m mouse

n n nest

o o orange

p p panda

q q queen

r r rabbit

s s sun

t t tiger

u u umbrella

v v van

w w watch

x x x-ray

y y yellow

z z zebra

Beginning with s

Trace the letter **s** with a pencil.

I spy with my little eye something beginning with **s**. Draw a ring around each object that starts with **s**.

Which object does not start with **s**? Draw a cross through the object.

Note for parent: Play 'I spy' with your child at home to encourage them to look for objects that start with different letter sounds.

Beginning with t

Trace the letter **t** with a pencil.

Name all the things on the shopping list. What sound do they all start with?

Note for parent: Go for a walk with your child and look for things beginning with the sound 't'.

9

Letter sound **p**

Trace the letter **p** with a pencil.

Listen for the sound **p** at the start of the words:

Peter picked a pot of purple plums.

Name the objects. Draw a ring around each object that starts with **p**. Draw a cross through each object that does not start with **p**.

Note for parent: This activity gives more practice in listening for and saying beginning sounds.

Trace the letter **b** with a pencil.

Listen for the sound **b** at the start of the words:

Billy eats berries and beetles for breakfast.

Name the objects. Draw a ring around each object that starts with **b**. Draw a cross through each object that does not start with **b**.

Note for parent: Encourage your child to say the sound of the letter, not its name – 'p' is 'p-p-puh', not 'pee', and 'b' is 'b-b-buh', not 'bee'.

11

Letter sound i

Trace the letter **i** with a pencil.
Put the dot on last.

Say the sound of each letter, then blend
the sounds together to read each word.

Listen for the sound **i** in the middle of the words.
Draw a ring around each word that contains **i**.

Dip, dip, dip,
My little ship,
Big cup and saucer,
Bobbing on the water.
Dip, dip, dip,
My little ship!

Note for parent: Say the short sound of 'i' as in 'insect', not the long sound as in 'ice'. 'Blend' is a
word that teachers use with children to describe how we join sounds in words.

Letter sound n

Trace the letter **n** with a pencil.

Listen for the sound **n** at the start and end of the words. Draw a ring around the letter **n** in each word.

net	pen	nut

bun	ten	sun

Colour the pictures.

Note for parent: These activities help your child to listen for sounds at the start, in the middle and at the end of words.

13

Word building with a

Trace the letter **a** with a pencil.

Write the letter **a** in the middle of the words. Then read each word.

b ☐ t	c a ☐ p
p a ☐ n	c ☐ n
d a ☐ d	v ☐ n
t ☐ p	m ☐ p
b ☐ g	j ☐ m

The letter **a** is also a little word by itself. For example:

a cat    a rat

Note for parent: Say the short sound of 'a' as in 'apple', not the long sound as in 'angel'.

Word building with e and o

Say the sound of each letter, then blend the sounds together to read each word.

Draw a ring around the word that matches each picture.

p-e-t   p-o-t

r-e-d   r-o-d

l-e-g   l-o-g

n-e-t   n-o-t

b-e-g   b-o-g

s-t-e-p   s-t-o-p

Note for parent: Say the short sound of 'e' as in 'egg', not the long sound as in 'eagle'. Say the short sound of 'o' as in 'on', not the long sound as in 'open'.

15

Word building with u

Trace the letter **u** with a pencil.

Listen for the sound **u** in the middle of the words:

Rub-a-dub-dub,
Three pugs in a tub!

Say the sound of each letter, then blend the sounds together to read each word.

h-u-t   r-u-b   c-u-p   d-u-b

t-u-b   b-u-t   s-u-m

Draw a ring around each word that is in the rhyme above.

Word building with **o** and **i**

Say the sound of each letter, then blend the sounds together to read each word. **ck** makes the sound **k** in all these words.

Draw a line to match each word to the correct picture.

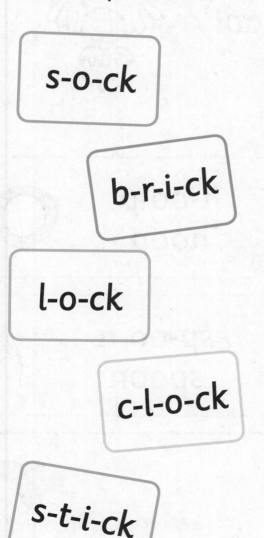

s-o-ck

b-r-i-ck

l-o-ck

c-l-o-ck

s-t-i-ck

Note for parent: Say the short sound of 'i' as in 'inventor', not the long sound as in 'idea'.
Say the short sound of 'o' as in 'otter', not the long sound as in 'oval'.

17

Double oo

Two **o**s together can make a long **oo** sound.

Say:

Try to read the words yourself.

**m-oo-n
moon**

**h-oo-p
hoop**

**b-oo-t
boot**

**sp-oo-n
spoon**

**l-oo-p
loop**

Note for parent: This activity helps your child hear sounds in words. Encourage your child to think of other words that include the 'oo' sound.

ch, sh and th

Say:

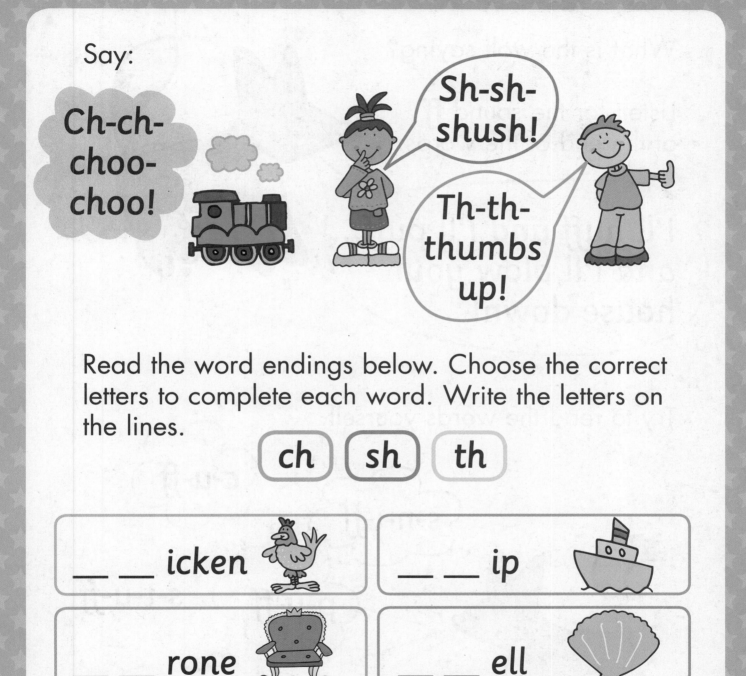

Ch-ch-choo-choo!

Sh-sh-shush!

Th-th-thumbs up!

Read the word endings below. Choose the correct letters to complete each word. Write the letters on the lines.

ch   sh   th

___ ___ icken

___ ___ ip

___ ___ rone

___ ___ ell

___ ___ eese

___ ___ umb

Note for parent: Help your child to read each of the word endings, then choose the correct starting sound. Help them write the letters in the spaces.

19

Double **ff**

What is the wolf saying?

Listen for the sound **ff** at the end of the words:

I'll huff and I'll puff... and I'll blow your house down!

Try to read the words yourself.

s-n-i-ff

c-u-ff

p-u-ff

s-t-u-ff

c-l-i-ff

f-l-u-ff

Double **ss**

What is the snake saying?

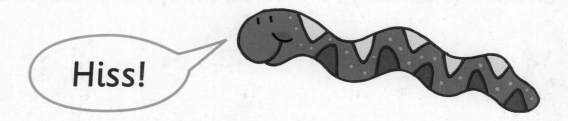

Try to read the words yourself.

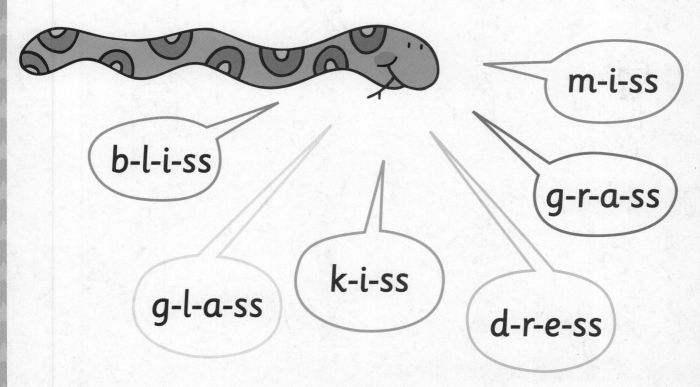

Colour each speech bubble that has a word that ends with **iss**.

Note for parent: Ask your child: 'Can you make up a sentence with any of these words in it?'

21

Trace each capital letter with a pencil. Say the name of each letter as you would recite it in the alphabet.

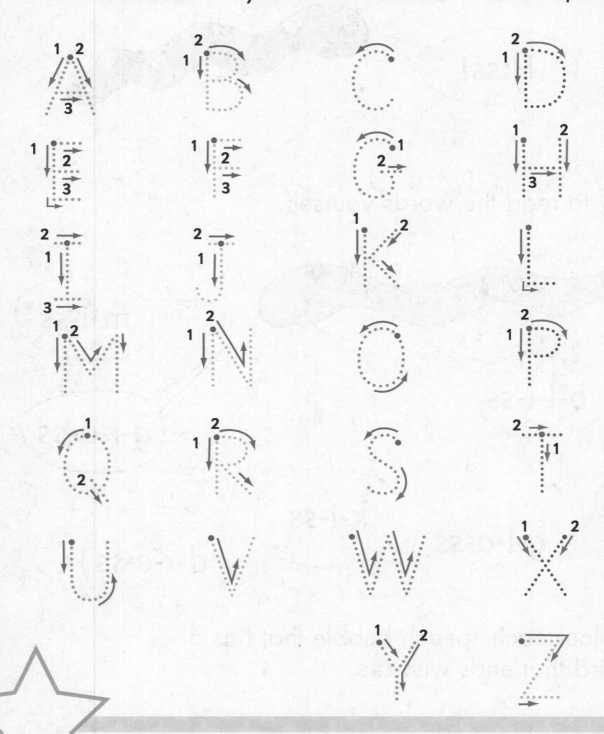

Note for parent: Each letter in the alphabet has a name and a sound. When you refer to capital letters, say the letter names, and when you refer to small letters, say the letter sounds.

We use capital letters to begin the names of people, places, days and months. We also use them to begin sentences.

Point to each capital letter in the invite below. Write your name on the dotted line using a capital letter at the start.

Ben's birthday party
On: Sunday 30th April
At: 2 Bath Street

To: ....

Please come to my party!

Key words

Some words are not easy to blend. You need to learn these words by memory. See if you can remember these useful words:

the | was | I | my | no | to | go

Read the story below. Trace over the words with a pencil to complete the story.

It was a cold morning.

I put on my hat.

I went to the shop for milk.

But the shop did not have milk.

I had to go home.

Note for parent: Point out the use of capital letters at the start of sentences. Explain that you use 'I' when you talk about yourself.

Read the sentences below. Choose the correct word to complete each sentence. Write the words on the lines.

am   at   on

I ____ five.

I ____ good ____ reading.

I can read the words ____ this page.

Now try to read the sentences yourself. Trace over the words with a pencil to complete the sentences.

I am five.

I am good at reading.
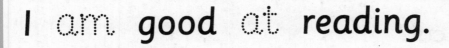

I can read the words on this page.

Read the labels.

**a hen
in a pen**

**a dog
in the fog**

**a cat
on a mat**

Answer these questions about the labels.
Draw a ring around each correct answer.

Where is the dog?

on a mat	in the fog	in a pen

Where is the hen?

in the fog	on a mat	in a pen

Where is the cat?

in a pen	on a mat	in the fog

Read the directions

Read the directions.

Get off the bus.

Go down the path.

Go up to the top of the hill.

Go in the cave.

Get the gold!

Now see how many directions you can remember from memory.

Rhyming words

Words that rhyme have the same ending sounds.

Listen for the sound **at** at the end of the words:

Rat-a-tat-tat!
Who is that?

A cat in
a hat!

Read the words on the hats. Draw a ring
around each word that ends with **at**.

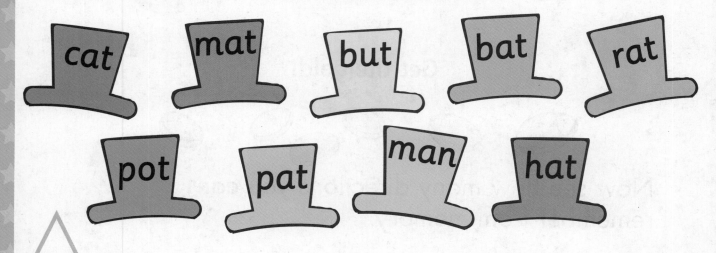

cat mat but bat rat

pot pat man hat

Note for parent: Look for books with predictable rhymes to read with your child. Stop reading when you come to the rhyming word and ask your child to guess which word it will be.

Read the words on the stepping stones. Draw a ring around each word that ends with **ail**.

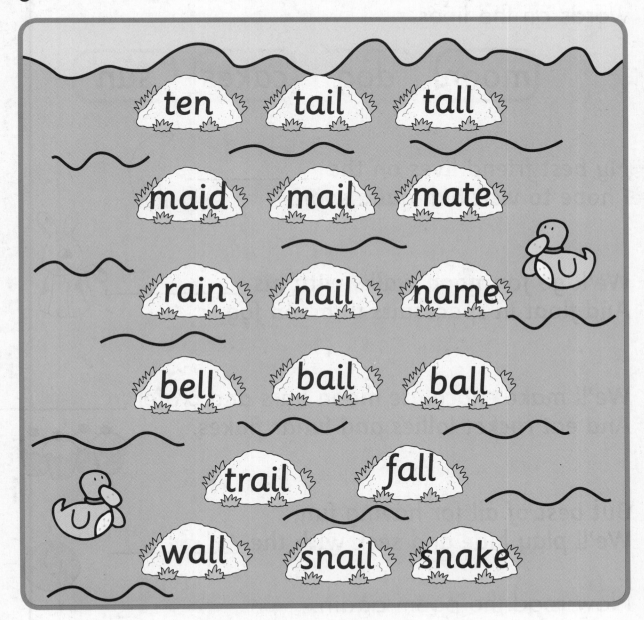

Now colour all the rhyming **ail** stones to make a path across the water.

Note for parent: Say a simple word such as 'dog', 'rug' or 'red' and see how many words your child can say that rhyme with it!

29

Read the poem

Read the poem. Look at the picture and choose the correct word to complete each sentence. Write the words on the lines.

moon   dog   cakes   sun

My best friend lives on the _____.
I hope to visit him quite soon.

We'll go for moon walks with his _____,
And float in spacesuits in moon fog.

We'll make chocolate moon bars and crater _____,
And eat rocket lollies and lunar flakes.

But best of all for having fun,
We'll play hide and seek with the _____.

Now read the poem again.

Note for parent: Stop when you come to the missing word and ask your child to guess the word.

Answer these questions about the poem.
Draw a ring around each correct answer.

Where does the best friend live?

| in the sea | on a farm | on the moon |

Who will they go for moon walks with?

| his dog | his cat | his rabbit |

Who will they play hide and seek with?

| the moon | the stars | the sun |

Answers

Page 8

Apple does not start with **s**.

Page 9

Tiger, toothbrush, tent, train, tie, tractor.
They all start with **t**.

Page 10

Pig, mouse, pear, duck, penguin, pen, panda.

Mouse and duck do not start with **p**.

Page 11

Bell, butterfly, cake, banana, frog, bath, bee.

Frog and cake do not start with **b**.

Page 12

(Dip, dip, dip,)
My (little ship,)
(Big) cup and saucer,
(Bobbing) on the water.
(Dip, dip, dip,)
My (little ship!)

Page 13

(net) pen (nut)
bun ten (sun)

Page 14

bat   cap
pan   can
dad   van
tap   map
bag   jam

Page 15

pet (pot)   (red) rod
leg (log)   (net) not
beg (bog)   (step) stop

Page 16

h-u-t   (r-u-b)   c-u-p   (d-u-b)
(t-u-b)   b-u-t   s-u-m

Page 17

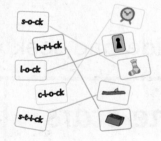

s-o-ck
b-r-i-ck
l-o-ck
c-l-o-ck
s-t-i-ck

Page 19

chicken   ship
throne   shell
cheese   thumb

Page 21

hiss   b-l-i-ss   k-i-ss   m-i-ss

Page 25

I **am** five.
I **am** good **at** reading.
I can read the words
on this page.

Page 26

The dog is in the fog.
The hen is in a pen.
The cat is on a mat.

Page 28

(cat) (mat) but (bat) (rat)
pot (pat) man (hat)

Page 29

ten (tail) tall
maid (mail) mate
rain (nail) name
bell (bail) ball
(trail) fall
wall (snail) snake

Page 30

My best friend lives on the **moon**.
I hope to visit him quite soon.
We'll go for moon walks with his **dog**,
And float in spacesuits in moon fog.
We'll make chocolate moon bars and crater **cakes**,
And eat rocket lollies and lunar flakes.
But best of all for having fun,
We'll play hide and seek with the **sun**.

Page 31

The best friend lives on the moon.
They will go for moon walks with his dog.
They will play hide and seek with the sun.